Usborne STEM

MATH

Scribble Book

THE MATH IN THIS BOOK WAS SCRIBBLED BY:

Written by
ALICE JAMES,
EDDIE REYNOLDS &
DARRAN STOBBART

Illustrated by
PETRA BAAN

Designed by
Emily Barden

Series editor Rosie Dickins

Series designer Zoe Wray

American editor Carrie Armstrong

Expert advice from
SHEILA EBBUTT &
STEPHEN JONES

CONTENTS

Solve number problems.

2 +

− 14

3 ×

6

= 78

Discover patterns that go on forever.

Design your own map.

Draw beautiful spirals.

Perform math magic tricks.

Make an infinite loop.

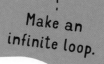

WHAT IS MATH?

Math is the study of NUMBERS, SHAPES and PATTERNS.
You're doing math all the time, every day. It's used for everything
from money and time, to music, art and sports.

These are some of the questions math can help to answer:

What's the **BIGGEST** number?

How heavy/long/tall/deep is this?

How do you measure time?

How do you draw 3-D shapes?

Can people predict how prices are going to change?

Which musical notes sound best together?

How many euros are there in a dollar?

What path is Earth taking around the Sun?

What will the world's population be in 2035?

How **FAST** can the internet get?

Math is incredibly varied – and so are people! So you may find some of the activities in this book harder or easier than other ones. That's OK – everyone's brain works a bit differently. Use the answers in the back if you need to – and have fun!

WHAT'S IN THIS BOOK?

Math isn't just about things to calculate.
This book is also full of things to:

SOL VE

INVEST IGATE

Imagine

DRAW

EXPLORE

Wherever you see a box with a lightbulb like this, you'll find an extra question to stretch your brain.

WHAT WILL YOU NEED?

For most of the book, you'll only need this book and a pencil. Occasionally you might need paper, glue or clear tape, a ruler and scissors. It'll be useful to have a calculator, too.

USBORNE QUICKLINKS

To download copies of the templates in this book, and for links to websites with more math facts and activities, go to **www.usborne.com/quicklinks** and type in the keywords: 'scribble math'. Please follow the online safety guidelines at the Usborne Quicklinks website.

PENTOMINO PROBLEMS

PENTOMINOES are shapes made up of 5 squares joined together, like this...

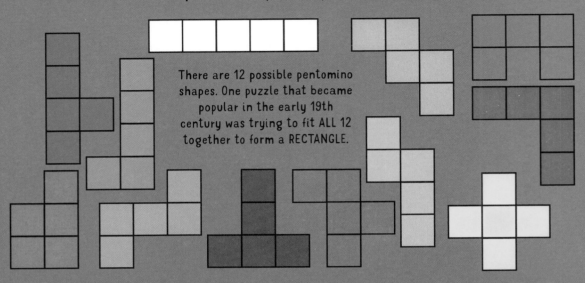

There are 12 possible pentomino shapes. One puzzle that became popular in the early 19th century was trying to fit ALL 12 together to form a RECTANGLE.

Here's a partly completed rectangle. Which pentominoes are missing? Figure out how they fit into the empty spaces, and shade them in to complete the puzzle.

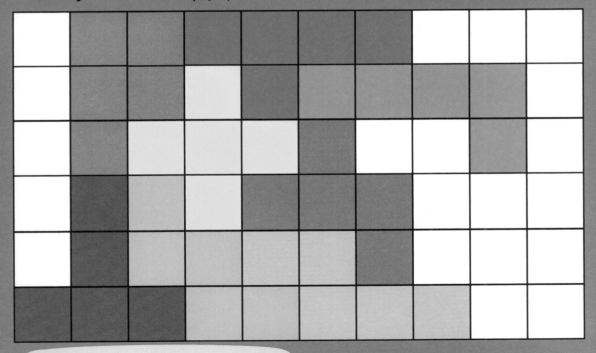

TIP: The remaining pentominoes may need to be rotated or flipped to fit in.

Fill in this rectangle with YOUR OWN arrangement of ALL 12 pentominoes.

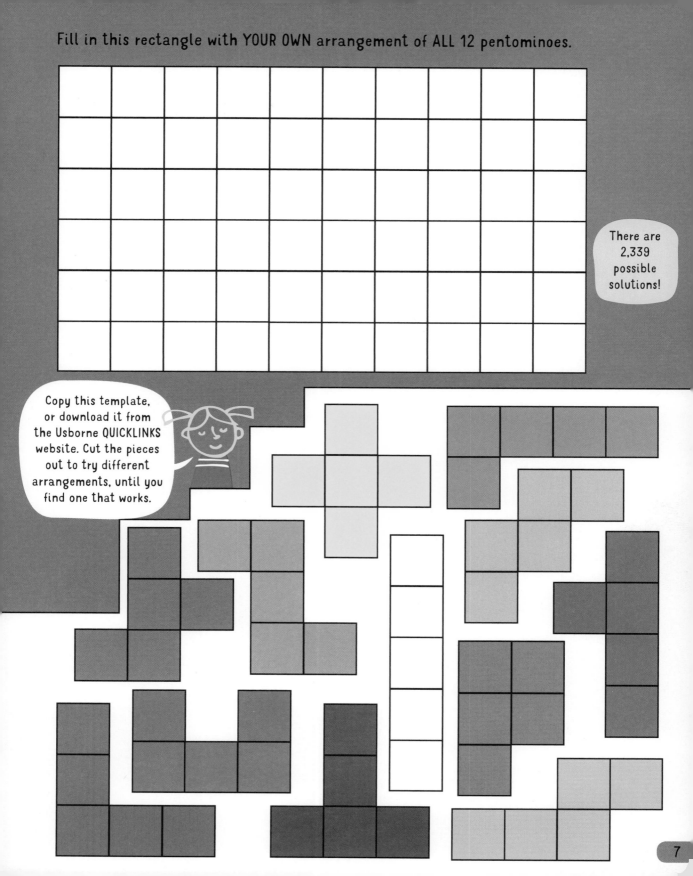

There are 2,339 possible solutions!

Copy this template, or download it from the Usborne QUICKLINKS website. Cut the pieces out to try different arrangements, until you find one that works.

Here's another shape. See if you can arrange all the pentominoes inside it.

TIP: To fit them all in, some of the pentominoes may need ROTATING, FLIPPING, or BOTH.

NUMBER BUILDER

For each of these puzzles, use the numbers on red bricks and the operations ➕ ➖ ✖ ➗ to try to end up with the number in the star. Scribble your workings in the spaces below. You can only use each number once, but you don't have to use them all.

EASY

2 45

5 20

1

⭐ 101

MEDIUM

6 12

5 9

2 4

⭐ 249

DIFFICULT

7

7

4 7

3

6

⭐ 95

SMALL WORLD

Mathematicians use something known as NETWORK THEORY to work out how CONNECTED people are to each other. One way to show these connections is by drawing a network that joins each person to all the other people they know.

Add lines to complete this network.

Halloa

TAMARA
(knows Jess and Arena)

JESS
(knows Tamara, Lena and Salome)

AYLIN
(knows Santiago)

Ciao

LENA
(knows Nico, Lola Jess and Santiago)

ARENA
(knows Tamara)

SALOME
(knows Jess and Nico)

NICO
(knows Lola, Salome and Lena)

Ola!

LOLA
(knows Lena, Nico, Maud and Bartosz)

SPREAD THE WORD

If Tamara sends a message to everybody she knows, and THEY then spread the message to everybody they know, and so on until everybody has heard the message - who will be the last to hear it?

TIP: Write '1' next to Tamara, then '2' next to everybody she knows, then '3' next to everybody THEY know, and so on, until there is only one person left.

EMMA
(knows Santiago)

QUINN
(knows Fenya, Sascha and Xue Lei)

Hi!

XUE LEI
(knows Quinn)

SANTIAGO
(knows Aylin, Jake, Emma and Lena)

SASCHA
(knows Quinn and Fenya)

¡Hola!

JAKE
(knows Maud and Santiago)

MAUD
(knows Lola, Jake and Jun)

FENYA
(knows Quinn, Sascha and Bartosz)

BARTOSZ
(knows Fenya and Lola)

Hej

KARL
(knows Jun)

JUN
(knows Maud and Karl)

LETTER CHAIN

A mathematician wants to send two letters to Karl. She gives a letter each to Nico and Quinn, and they hand them on to people they know until the letters reach Karl. The SHORTEST route from Nico is FOUR steps, and from Quinn it's SIX. Mark the routes on the network, or write them in the box on the right.

PLOTTING CURVES

Two sets of points have been marked out on the grid below. Connect pairs of points with the same number to complete the pattern. What shape do you get?

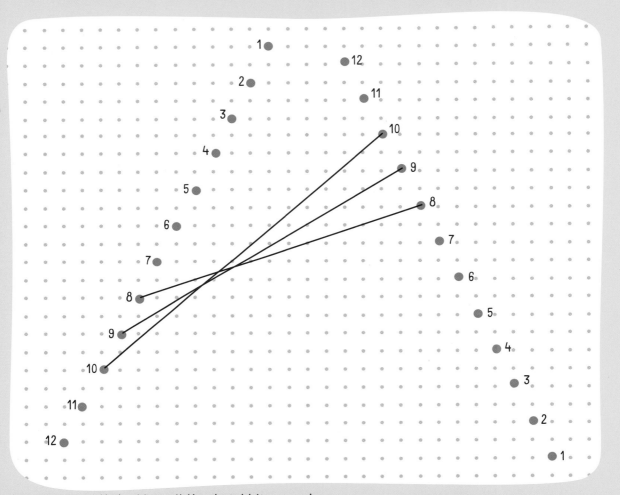

You should find that adding all the straight lines creates a CURVE. This type of curve is known as a PARABOLA.

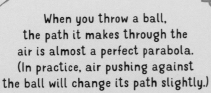

When you throw a ball, the path it makes through the air is almost a perfect parabola. (In practice, air pushing against the ball will change its path slightly.)

A rocket soaring into space to orbit the Earth follows a parabola-shaped path until it leaves the atmosphere.

Connecting points in DIFFERENT ARRANGEMENTS creates different curves and patterns. Try matching the numbers on the grid below.

On some graphs you can get more than one curve - the pattern on the right has two curves.

4 • 3 • 2 • 1 • • • 1 • 2 • 3 • 4

For any PAIR of points, one set counts DOWN towards the middle...

...and one set counts UP towards the middle.

Use this space to create your own arrangement of numbered points. Connect the matching numbers to see what curves you create.

You could try a SQUARE or a CROSS.

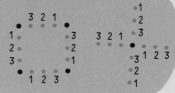

13

CRACKING CODES

You can hide letters and numbers by turning them into CODES.
You do this using a set of steps known as a CIPHER.

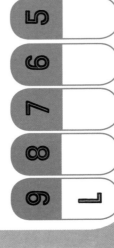

In some codes, numbers are changed into OTHER NUMBERS using a cipher. Try these:

Add 1 to each digit, then double it

2	4	6	8	10
6				

This is known as a TRANSPOSITION cipher.

Square each digit (multiply it by itself)

5	6	7	8	9
25				

This is known as a SUBSTITUTION cipher.

Add 3 to each digit, then turn it into its corresponding letter.

9	8	7	6	5
L				

In other codes, numbers are changed into LETTERS or SYMBOLS. Try these:

Turn each digit into its corresponding letter of the alphabet, using the code wheel on the left.

1	2	3	4	5
A				

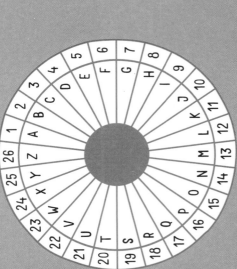

Here's a sequence:

19 18 23 23 22 13 26 4 26 2

It's been turned into three CODES:

What CIPHER has been used to create each of the codes?

17 16 21 21 20 11 24 2 24 0

40 38 48 48 46 28 54 10 54 6

H I D D E N A W A Y

Create your own coded version by inventing a new cipher.

In 2018 the British government used a code-breaking challenge to hire new spies.

INSIDE SHAPES

There are rules, or FORMULAS, for working out the area of any REGULAR shape, such as a square or an equilateral triangle like the one on the left. But what about an IRREGULAR shape?

Regular

Regular

Irregular

A mathematician named Georg Pick came up with a quick way to work out the area of any irregular straight-edged shape on a square grid. Here's how it works.

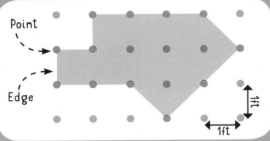

Point

Edge

STEP 1:

Count the number of points TOUCHING the EDGES of the shape, shown in red.

$\div 2 =$ ANSWER TO STEP 1

So here for example, 12 ÷ 2 = 6

If the distance between each point in a square on the grid is 1 foot, the area is measured in FEET SQUARED (ft²).

STEP 2:

ANSWER TO STEP 1 + The number of points INSIDE the shape, shown in green. $-1 =$ The area in feet squared.

6 + 4 - 1 = 9 ft²

Two people are thinking about buying a new shed. Can you calculate the AREA of this shed to figure out which person the shed is suited to?

I want the area to be over 20 ft².

Rosie

I want the area to be over 25 ft².

Scribble your working out here.

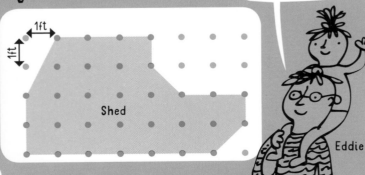

1ft

1ft

Shed

Eddie

MAKE A HOUSE A HOME

The owner wants to put the shed in a field. What else could they put there? Design it on the grid below. Make sure you include a vegetable garden. You could also add a hen coop, a pond and anything else, as long as all the edges are straight.

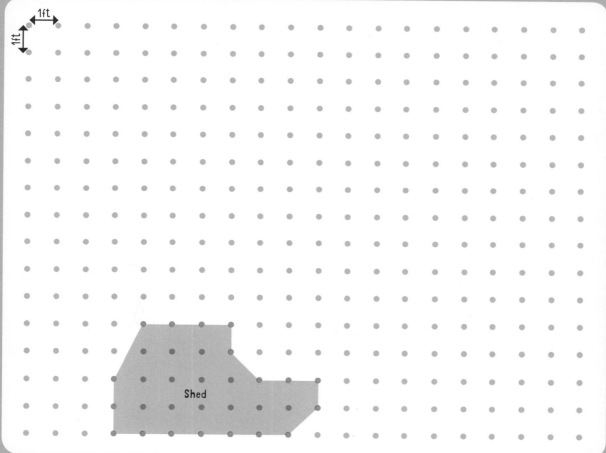

1ft

1ft

Shed

The shed owner wants to grow pumpkins in the vegetable garden. If each pumpkin plant needs 2 ft², how many will fit in the vegetable garden you designed?

TIP: Calculate the AREA of the vegetable garden, then divide it by 2.

MAGIC SQUARES

In a MAGIC SQUARE, every ROW, COLUMN and DIAGONAL adds up to the same value, and no numbers repeat.

Finish this magic square, so everything adds up to 15.

The square should contain the numbers 1-9. Each number should appear only once.

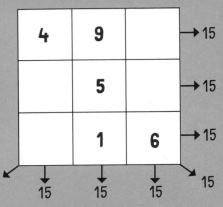

4	9		→ 15
	5		→ 15
	1	6	→ 15

15 ↓ 15 ↓ 15 ↓ 15 → 15 (diagonal) 15 ↙

Magic squares were once considered lucky. An Ancient Chinese legend tells how, in awful floods, the emperor saw a turtle with a magic square made of spots on its shell. Each line added up to 15, so the emperor gave the river gods 15 gifts – and the floods stopped.

Now finish these two bigger squares. Use the numbers 1-16, and make every row, column and diagonal add up to 34.

7		1	14
2			11
16	3	10	
	6		

2		12	
	9	6	3
			10
11	14	1	

See if you can work out a 5 x 5 magic square with rows, columns and diagonals that add up to 65.

ANGLE NAVIGATOR

Mathematicians use ANGLES to measure TURNS.
Sailors and pilots also use turns, along with
a compass, to keep track of directions.

Angles are measured
in DEGREES (°).
A FULL turn is 360°.

The angles
between 0° and
360° match up to
the points on a
COMPASS, like this. - - ->

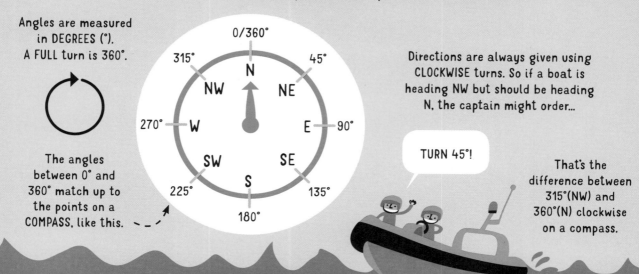

Directions are always given using
CLOCKWISE turns. So if a boat is
heading NW but should be heading
N, the captain might order...

TURN 45°!

That's the
difference between
315°(NW) and
360°(N) clockwise
on a compass.

A helicopter pilot sends instructions to the rescue boats on the map below,
to direct them to a sinking ferry. Draw straight lines from each boat
(shown in orange) in the direction it needs to head.

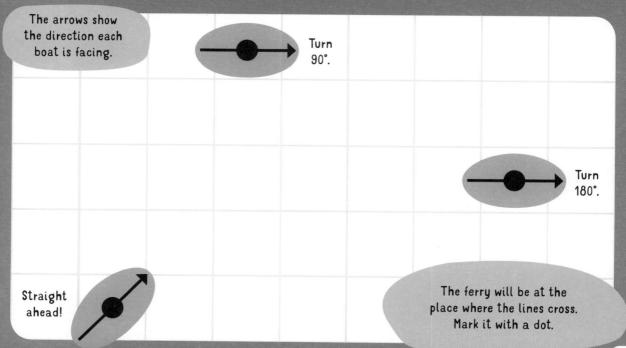

The arrows show
the direction each
boat is facing.

Turn
90°.

Turn
180°.

Straight
ahead!

The ferry will be at the
place where the lines cross.
Mark it with a dot.

RaNDoM NuMbERS

In math, RANDOM NUMBERS have no pattern or sequence - meaning it's impossible to tell what number will come next. TRULY random numbers are extremely difficult to generate.

Write down 10 numbers off the top of your head. Make them as mixed up and random as you can.

Those numbers might look very random, but however hard you try, they won't be COMPLETELY random - your brain works in a way that makes it impossible.

It's hard to tell if numbers are truly random just by looking. Often numbers that look random, actually aren't...

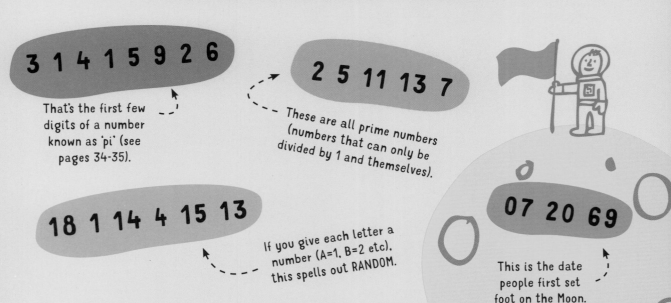

3 1 4 1 5 9 2 6

That's the first few digits of a number known as 'pi' (see pages 34-35).

2 5 11 13 7

These are all prime numbers (numbers that can only be divided by 1 and themselves).

18 1 14 4 15 13

If you give each letter a number (A=1, B=2 etc), this spells out RANDOM.

07 20 69

This is the date people first set foot on the Moon.

One way to generate random numbers is by ROLLING DICE.

If you don't have a dice, you can make one using the template below. Roll it 5 times and record the numbers in these circles.

LOTTERIES rely on totally random numbers.
Play a round of Scribble Lottery below. The five numbers you rolled, in that order, are the WINNING NUMBERS. Compare that sequence to these tickets.

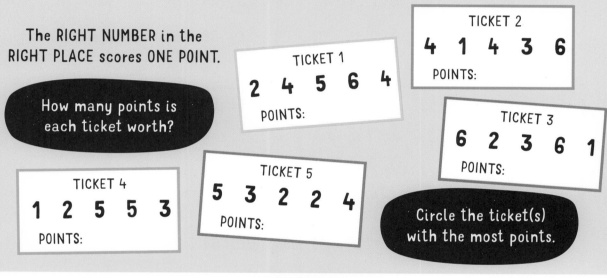

The RIGHT NUMBER in the RIGHT PLACE scores ONE POINT.

How many points is each ticket worth?

TICKET 1
2 4 5 6 4
POINTS:

TICKET 2
4 1 4 3 6
POINTS:

TICKET 3
6 2 3 6 1
POINTS:

TICKET 4
1 2 5 5 3
POINTS:

TICKET 5
5 3 2 2 4
POINTS:

Circle the ticket(s) with the most points.

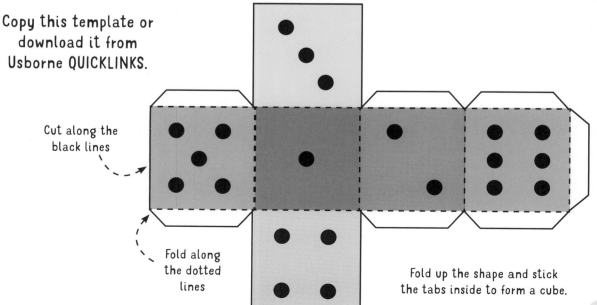

Copy this template or download it from Usborne QUICKLINKS.

Cut along the black lines

Fold along the dotted lines

Fold up the shape and stick the tabs inside to form a cube.

PRIME NUMBERS

PRIME NUMBERS are numbers that can ONLY be divided by two numbers – 1 AND themselves. Find and color in or circle the remaining prime numbers in the grid below. Altogether, there are 25 prime numbers between 1 and 100.

2 is the first prime number. It's the only prime that's an EVEN number.

1	2	3	4	5	6	7	8	9	10
11	12	13	14	15	16	17	18	19	20
21	22	23	24	25	26	27	28	29	30
31	32	33	34	35	36	37	38	39	40
41	42	43	44	45	46	47	48	49	50
51	52	53	54	55	56	57	58	59	60
61	62	63	64	65	66	67	68	69	70
71	72	73	74	75	76	77	78	79	80
81	82	83	84	85	86	87	88	89	90
91	92	93	94	95	96	97	98	99	100

TIP: Go through the times tables answers up to 100, and CROSS OUT any numbers that CAN'T be primes.

Mathematicians are always searching for bigger and bigger primes. The biggest found have over 20 MILLION digits.

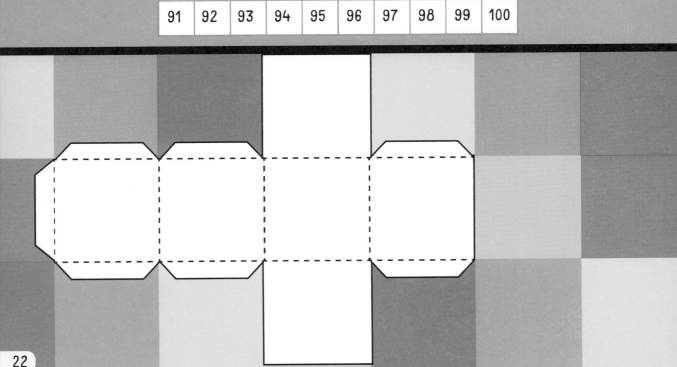

22

SQUARES AND CUBES

A SQUARE number is a number multiplied by itself.
A CUBE number is a number multiplied by itself TWICE.

2 X 2 = 4 — SQUARE number

2 X 2 X 2 = 8 — CUBE number

There is ONE number between 2 and 100 that is both a square AND a cube number. Use this space to work out what it is.

TIP: Work out the square numbers up to 100. Then work out the cube numbers until you find a match.

Can you find a THREE-DIGIT number that is both a square and a cube number?

23

EVERLASTING PATTERNS

Some patterns are what mathematicians call FRACTAL – as you zoom in closer, the pattern always REPEATS.
Theoretically you could zoom in forever and the pattern would always be the same.

One fractal shape is known as a SIERPINSKI TRIANGLE.
It's built like this:

1.
You start with an EQUILATERAL triangle.

2.
You add an upside-down triangle in the middle. All the triangles that are added will be upside down.

3.
You add smaller upside-down triangles around it.

4.
Then keep adding more triangles...

5.
...and more...

The corners of each new triangle always touch the edges of the triangle around it.

Continue drawing more triangles in this Sierpinski triangle.

In theory you could keep adding smaller and smaller triangles forever. (In practice they will become too tiny to draw.)

This fractal pattern is called a KOCH SNOWFLAKE. It's also made by adding triangles again and again, this time to the OUTSIDE...

Make your own Koch snowflake here, by adding more triangles.

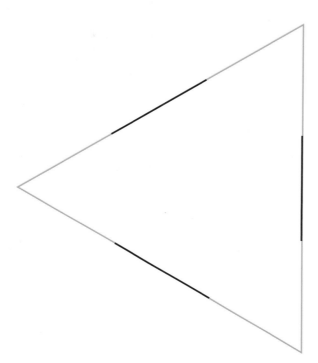

1. Start with an equilateral triangle.

2. Add smaller triangles to the sides.

3. Add more again...

4. ...and again...

MONEY, MONEY, MONEY

The type of money a country or region uses is known as its CURRENCY.
Currencies are broken down into units, or DENOMINATIONS.

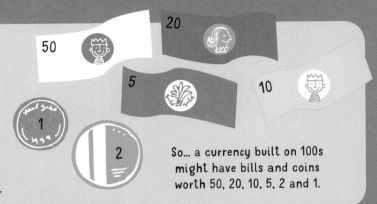

Most currencies work in UNITS of 100 (100 pennies in a pound, 100 cents in a euro or dollar). These are known as DECIMAL systems.

Coins and bills are always FACTORS of the main unit – meaning values that divide into it exactly. There's not always a coin for EVERY factor though.

So... a currency built on 100s might have bills and coins worth 50, 20, 10, 5, 2 and 1.

INVENT YOUR OWN CURRENCY

What units will your currency be built on?

What bills and coins will you have?

A currency built on 40s could have 40, 20, 10, 8, 5, 4, 2 and 1 coins.

A currency built on a PRIME NUMBER, such as 43, will only have 2 coins or bills – 43 and 1.

WHAT IS IT CALLED?

Krone Dollar Euro
Rupee Franc Yen Pound

You could give your currency a name, and design a symbol for it. Here are some example currencies, what is yours called?

£ $ ¥ €

CURRENCY NAME:

SYMBOL:

Describe your currency here:

There are .... in a ....

(e.g. There are 100 cents in a dollar.)

HOW DO YOU USE IT?

Imagine using your new currency. Which combinations of coins or bills would you need to make each of these values? Scribble them in the boxes.

84

27

66

13

MY MONEY

Are there any values you CAN'T make?

X MARKS THE SPOT

Mathematicians study patterns to see how RANDOM, or not, they are.
If a pattern IS random, mathematicians call it a 'RANDOM DISTRIBUTION'.
Follow the instructions on the right to try to create your own random pattern.

Use the grid on the left to investigate random distributions, like this:

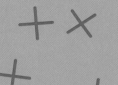

Wad a tiny piece of paper into a ball.

Stretch one hand up off the book, with your little finger on the page. Drop the ball onto the grid from that height, always from the same spot.

Mark an X where your ball lands. If it bounces off the page, just try again. Repeat this about 15 times.

Are the marks evenly spread or do they clump together? A random distribution is NOT evenly spread.

Where the ball lands is largely random, but you can never create a TRULY random distribution - the shape and weight of the paper ball, and how you drop it, will all have TINY EFFECTS that make it LESS random.

Humans tend to see patterns even in completely random things, for example, finding shapes in clouds...

Do these clouds remind you of anything? Scribble it here.

REP-TILES

Some shapes can be combined with several identical copies to create a larger version of the original shape. Shapes that can do this are known as REPLICATING TILES, or REP-TILES.

Squares can ALWAYS be rep-tiles – combining four squares will make a larger square.

Triangles can always be made into rep-tiles too.

2.5cm

5cm

There are three of these triangles below. Add TWO MORE to create a triangle the same shape, but BIGGER.

Tip: Each shape can be flipped over and/or rotated, but it has to stay the same size.

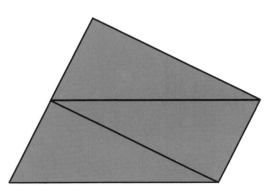

There are two more rep tiles at the bottom of this page. Work out how to combine each into a larger version, and scribble or stick your solutions in the boxes here and on the next page.

SHAPE 1

SHAPE 1

Copy these templates, or print them from the Usborne QUICKLINKS website, then cut out the pieces.

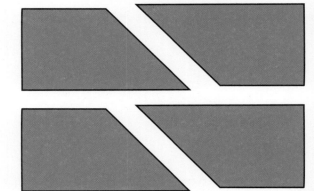

SHAPE 2

The answer box for this shape is on the next page.

The SIERPINSKI TRIANGLE on page 24 is another example of a rep-tile.

SHAPE 2

Turn back to page 31 for the instructions.

SHAPE 2

SHAPE 1

MAP MATH

In 1976, two mathematicians proved the FOUR COLOR THEOREM.
The theorem says it's possible to color ANY map with just FOUR colors,
so that NO shapes of the same color touch each other.

Try it yourself on this map.

Colors CAN touch
at POINTS if they have
to, as they do here.

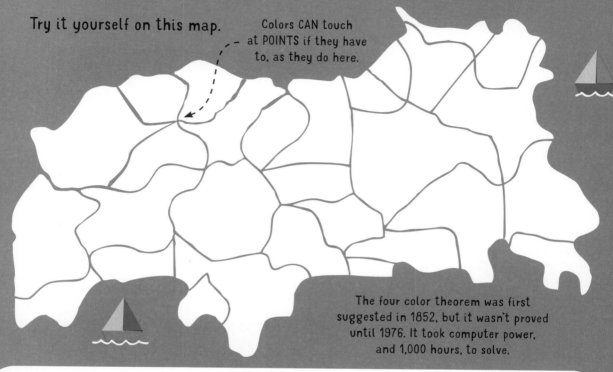

The four color theorem was first
suggested in 1852, but it wasn't proved
until 1976. It took computer power,
and 1,000 hours, to solve.

DRAW YOUR OWN MAP

Then see if you can fill it in following
the four color theorem.

DISCOVER PI

Thousands of years ago, mathematicians discovered one particular value kept cropping up when working with circles. The value became known as **pi**, with the symbol **π**. See how it works for yourself...

TO FIND PI

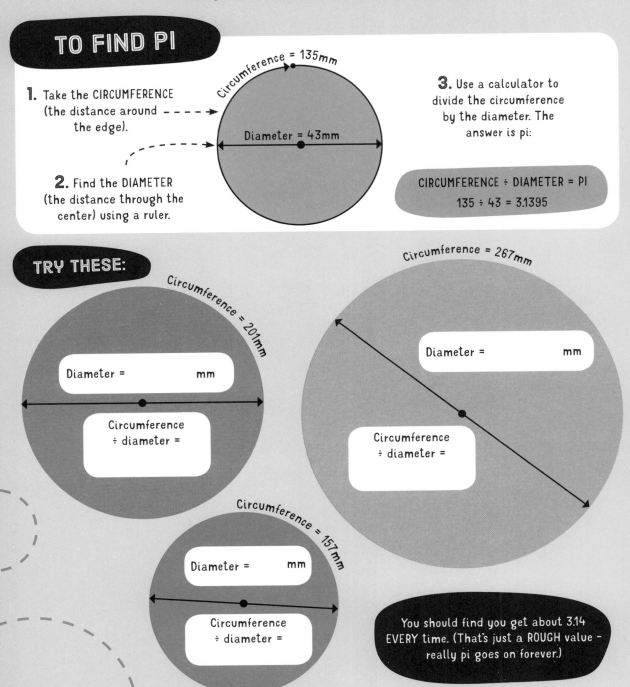

1. Take the CIRCUMFERENCE (the distance around the edge).

2. Find the DIAMETER (the distance through the center) using a ruler.

Circumference = 135mm

Diameter = 43mm

3. Use a calculator to divide the circumference by the diameter. The answer is pi:

CIRCUMFERENCE ÷ DIAMETER = PI
135 ÷ 43 = 3.1395

TRY THESE:

Circumference = 201mm

Diameter =   mm

Circumference ÷ diameter =

Circumference = 267mm

Diameter =   mm

Circumference ÷ diameter =

Circumference = 157mm

Diameter =   mm

Circumference ÷ diameter =

You should find you get about 3.14 EVERY time. (That's just a ROUGH value – really pi goes on forever.)

PIEMS

Some people make up poems known as PIEMS (pi poems) to help them remember pi. Look at the one below, then try making up your own.

The first 12 digits of pi are:
3.14159265358

The first digit is 3, so the first word of the poem has three letters.

YOUR TURN
Make sure each word has the right number of letters.

3.	Hey!
1	A
4	TRex!
1	A
5	Beast
9	Trampling
2	My
6	Plants!
5	Leave,
3	You
5	Pesky
8	Dinosaur.

Next is 1, so a one-letter word. And so on...

Add punctuation wherever you like.

3.	_____
1	_____
4	_____
1	_____
5	_____
9	_____
2	_____
6	_____
5	_____
3	_____
5	_____
8	_____

THUD

FINDING YOUR WAY

When someone asks a phone or GPS system for directions, that machine uses a piece of math known as DIJKSTRA'S* ALGORITHM to find the quickest way.

HOW DOES IT WORK?

In Dijkstra's algorithm, a map is imagined as a series of dots, known as NODES, and paths between them known as EDGES. The graph won't be an exact match of any map – it's a simplification.

← - - - NODE

- - - EDGE

A

7

D

B

4

7

3

2

E

9

C

2

2

1

2

G

6

F

Each edge has a NUMBER on it that represents how LONG it is.

The combination of edges with the SMALLEST total will be the QUICKEST route.

For example, the quickest way to get from A to G on this map is:

A — 7 — D — 3 — C — 1 — G

...which adds up to

11

WHICH IS QUICKEST?

Here's another map. Which route is quicker between A and G below – green or yellow?

A-B-C-E-G =

A-D-F-G =

*Pronounced 'dike-stra'

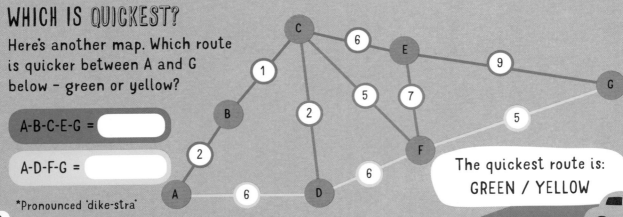

C

6

E

9

G

1

5

5

B

2

7

A

2

F

6

5

6

D

The quickest route is: GREEN / YELLOW

TRY IT YOURSELF
On this map, the shortest route from A to J
has a total length of 19. What is the route?

Use this space to scribble any
working out.

START

A — 5 — B

12

6

2

1

E

C

D

39

16

2

6

7

7

G

F

3

11

23

H

I

8

8

J ← FINISH

THE SHORTEST ROUTE IS:

A
J

BEEP

Computers can calculate the
shortest route across the roads of
an ENTIRE country in seconds.

The Fibonacci sequence

In 1202, Italian mathematician Leonardo Fibonacci worked out
a sequence of numbers based on the following rule.

RULE: Each number is
the SUM of the previous two.

Continue the sequence below.

0+1 =   1+2 =

$$0, 1, 1, 2, 3, 5, ..., ..., ..., ..., ...$$

1+1 =   2+3 =

This Fibonacci sequence pops up again and again in nature - for example
numbers of tree branches. Try it yourself on the tree below.

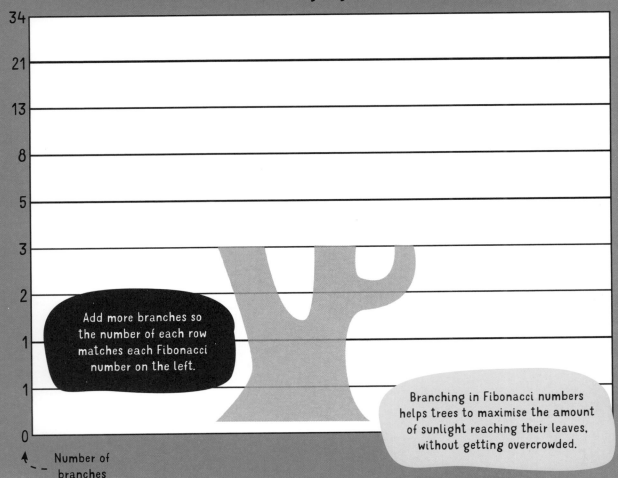

34

21

13

8

5

3

2

1

Add more branches so
the number of each row
matches each Fibonacci
number on the left.

1

0

↑ Number of
‾ ‾ branches

Branching in Fibonacci numbers
helps trees to maximise the amount
of sunlight reaching their leaves,
without getting overcrowded.

The Fibonacci sequence is often found in seeds and leaves, too.
COUNT the numbers of SPIRALS on the aloe plant and pinecone below.

Some spirals are colored to help you see where they are.

ALOE

SPIRALS:

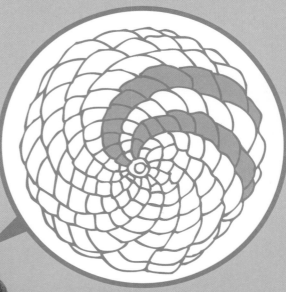

PINECONE

SPIRALS:

The NUMBER OF SPIRALS will be a number in the FIBONACCI SEQUENCE.

Add together any three consecutive numbers in the Fibonacci sequence. Do you notice anything?

Fibonacci spirals

The Fibonacci SEQUENCE is also behind a shape called the Fibonacci SPIRAL — another pattern found throughout nature.

STEP 1: BUILD A RECTANGLE

Start with a square, with a side length of 1.

Add increasingly bigger squares, where the lengths of the sides are numbers in the Fibonacci sequence.

Add them in the order shown by the arrows – in a spiral shape from the first square.

⬜ 1   ⬜⬜ 1 1

Add another 1x1 square to form a rectangle.

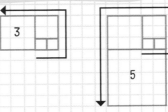

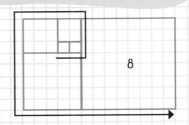

STEP 2: DRAW IN THE SPIRAL

Draw a curve between the opposite corners of each square, like this:

Continue the spiral by following the points in the corners of each box.

Fibonacci spirals are found throughout the animal kingdom. Fill in the spirals between the blue dots on these creatures.

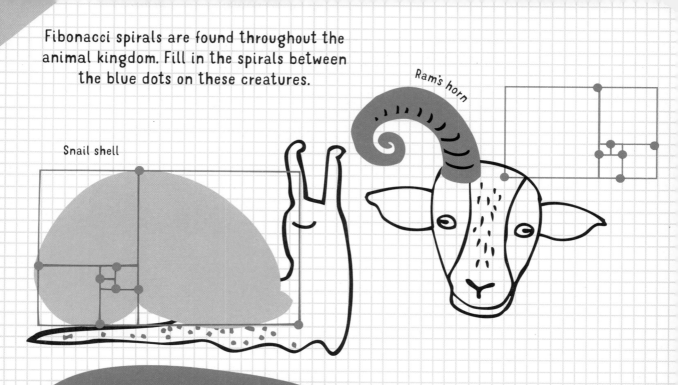

Ram's horn

Snail shell

Create your own rectangle below, then add the spiral. Draw in a creature too, if you like.

TIP: Look back at the Fibonacci sequence you wrote out on page 38 to see how big each new square needs to be.

BIG NUMBERS

There's a set of rules, known as the CONWAY-WECHSLER SYSTEM, for working out the names of really HUGE numbers. Imagine an ENORMOUS number, with one to two THOUSAND zeros. Follow the simplified steps here to find out what it is called.

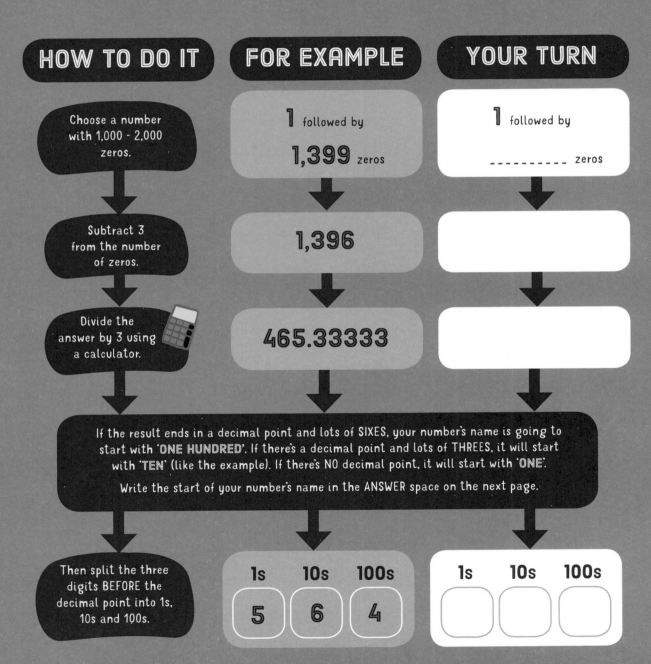

HOW TO DO IT

Choose a number with 1,000 - 2,000 zeros.

Subtract 3 from the number of zeros.

Divide the answer by 3 using a calculator.

If the result ends in a decimal point and lots of SIXES, your number's name is going to start with 'ONE HUNDRED'. If there's a decimal point and lots of THREES, it will start with 'TEN' (like the example). If there's NO decimal point, it will start with 'ONE'.

Write the start of your number's name in the ANSWER space on the next page.

Then split the three digits BEFORE the decimal point into 1s, 10s and 100s.

FOR EXAMPLE

1 followed by **1,399** zeros

1,396

465.33333

1s	10s	100s
5	6	4

YOUR TURN

1 followed by _____ zeros

1s	10s	100s

Now look at the table below. Find the term for the number of 1s you had in the last step, and circle it. Then do the same for the number of 10s and the number of 100s.

	1s	10s	100s
0	–	–	–
1	UN	DECI	CENTILLION
2	DUO	VIGINTI	DUCENTILLION
3	TRE	TRIGINTA	TRECENTILLION
4	QUATTUOR	QUADRAGINTA	(QUADRINGENTILLION)
5	(QUIN)	QUINQUAGINTA	QUINGENTILLION
6	SES	(SEXAGINTA)	SESCENTILLION
7	SEPTEM	SEPTUAGINTA	SEPTINGENTILLION
8	OCTO	OCTOGINTA	OCTINGENTILLION
9	NOVEM	NONAGINTA	NONGENTILLION

The words in the table all come from LATIN – an ancient language often used by scholars.

Add the terms you circled after the first word, to write out your number's full name.

TEN QUIN-SEXAGINTA-QUADRINGENTILLION

ANSWER

WHAT'S IT FOR?

The number you named is really, REALLY big. What could you use a number that big to count or measure?

Milliliters of water on Earth?

Atoms in the universe?

Kilometers from Earth to the edge of the Milky Way?

MICRO to TERA

Different things can be measured in different METRIC UNITS. Mathematicians have names for each of the units. PREFIXES make those units bigger or smaller, from the VERY TINY to the ABSOLUTELY HUGE.

> I'm 5 and a half MILLION micrometers tall...

> Let's measure you in meters!

METERS are the basic unit of length.

Fill the boxes with scribbles of things you could sensibly measure with each of these units.

MICROMETERS

Human body cells

Bacteria

MILLIMETERS

Small insects

CENTIMETERS

Objects you can hold

People

METERS

Buildings

Swimming pools

MICRO
1,000x smaller than milli

MILLI
10x smaller than centi

CENTI
100x smaller than the basic unit

BASIC UNIT

BYTES are the basic unit of computer storage.
(1 byte is enough to store 8 individual digits.)

(A) KILOBYTES
1,000 bytes*

(B) MEGABYTES
1,000,000 bytes

(C) GIGABYTES
1,000,000,000 bytes

(D) TERABYTES
1,000,000,000,000 bytes

Which of these units might be
best to measure the following?
Add a letter in each circle below.

The memory capacity
of a smartphone

All the memories a
human brain can hold

A big photo or
music file

A page of
text

Can you convert each of the following to powers?

KILOBYTE: 1,000 bytes = 10^3

MEGABYTE: 1,000,000 bytes = _ _ _ _ _ _

GIGABYTE: 1,000,000,000 bytes = _ _ _ _ _ _

TERABYTE: 1,000,000,000,000 bytes = _ _ _ _ _ _

*A number with lots of
zeros can also be written
as a POWER like this:
10^3 means a 1 followed
by 3 zeros.

KILO
1,000x
bigger than
the basic unit

MEGA
1,000x
bigger
than kilo

GIGA
1,000x
bigger
than mega

TERA
1,000x
bigger
than giga

Pattern hunting

This is a SEQUENCE of numbers known as PASCAL'S TRIANGLE.

The triangle starts with 1s.

The numbers in the shapes in each new row are made by adding together the numbers above it.

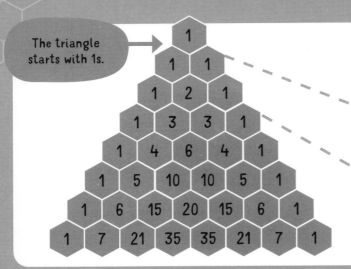

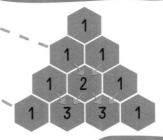

So numbers on the outside of the triangle always remain as 1.

Mathematicians find all sorts of number patterns in this triangle. Investigate some of them for yourself.

Add together the numbers in each row of the triangle.

Put your answers next to each row.

Use this space for working out.

Do you spot a pattern?

HMMM

46

If you add all the yellow numbers together, the answer is the green number.

This one is known as a HOCKEY STICK PATTERN because of its shape. Find and color more hockey stick patterns on this triangle.

CLUNK

Finish off this Pascal's triangle.

Then color all the ODD numbers the same color.

Take a look at page 24 – do you recognize your Pascal pattern?

47

TAKING A WALK

In the 18th century, mathematician Leonhard Euler was set a challenge by the town of Königsberg. To answer it, Euler developed a completely new type of mathematics, known as GRAPH THEORY.

MAP OF KÖNIGSBERG

THE CHALLENGE

Königsberg has 7 bridges. Is it possible to walk through the town, crossing EVERY BRIDGE once and ONLY once?

To work it out, Euler turned the map of Königsberg into a GRAPH made of dots and lines.

The dots – known as NODES – represent areas within Königsberg.

GRAPH OF KÖNIGSBERG

The lines – or EDGES – connecting the nodes represent the routes across the bridges.

Can you find a route that visits every node, going along each edge ONLY ONCE?

YES / NO

Euler found the challenge was IMPOSSIBLE. He also discovered a RULE to work out whether a path would be possible or impossible for ANY graph.

EULER'S RULE: To have a path which uses every edge ONLY ONCE, the graph must have either ZERO or TWO nodes with an ODD number of edges attached.

This graph has ZERO nodes WITH AN ODD NUMBER OF EDGES, so there IS a route.

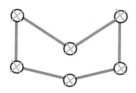

This path has TWO nodes with an odd number of edges so there IS a route.

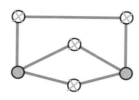

In Königsberg, all four nodes have an odd number of edges, so there is NO route that works.

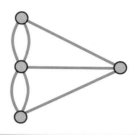

⊗ Even   ◯ Odd

Here are two more graphs. Use Euler's rule to work out if they have a route around them, using every edge just once.

Start here

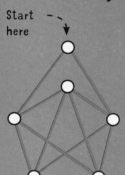

NUMBER OF NODES WITH AN ODD NUMBER OF EDGES:

- - - - - - - - - - - - -

IS THERE A POSSIBLE ROUTE?
YES / NO

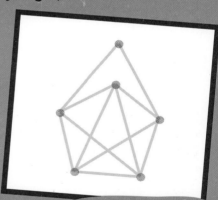

TIP: Shade in the nodes with odd edges, and put an X in the nodes with even edges, to make them easy to count.

Try drawing over these maps to check your answer.

Start here

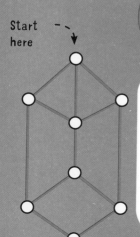

NUMBER OF NODES WITH AN ODD NUMBER OF EDGES:

- - - - - - - - - - - - -

IS THERE A POSSIBLE ROUTE?
YES / NO

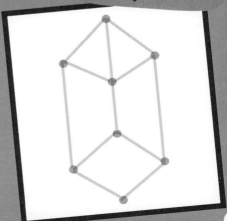

Add bridges to this map to create a layout where there IS a route that crosses each bridge once and only once.

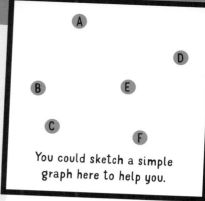

You could sketch a simple graph here to help you.

A

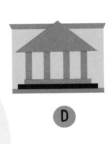

D

E

B

C

F

Remember, you can make your layout as complicated as you like, but it must have either ZERO or TWO nodes with an ODD number of edges.

THE PUZZLE SOLVED AT LAST

Today it IS possible to walk through Königsberg crossing each bridge only once. This is because two bridges were destroyed in the Second World War, leaving only two nodes with an odd number of edges.

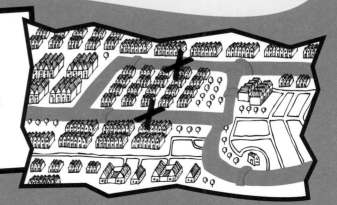

PERFECT NUMBERS

Perfect numbers are all about FACTORS. A number's FACTORS are other numbers that divide into it exactly, leaving no remainders. When a number's factors add up to the number itself, it's said to be PERFECT.

FACTORS OF 6:

$6 \div 6 = \textcircled{1}$ $6 \div 3 = \textcircled{2}$
$6 \div 2 = \textcircled{3}$

One factor is always the number itself, but you don't use the original number when trying to find perfect numbers.

Work out which of the numbers on this page are perfect.

6

FACTORS: 6, 3, 2, 1

SUM: 3 + 2 + 1 = 6

PERFECT? YES

12

FACTORS: _____

SUM: _____

PERFECT? _____

28

FACTORS: _____

SUM: _____

PERFECT? _____

50

FACTORS: _____

SUM: _____

PERFECT? _____

36

FACTORS: _____

_____

_____

SUM: _____

PERFECT? _____

TESSELLATIONS

A pattern made up of repeating shapes, fitting together without any gaps, is known as a TESSELLATION.

Tessellations can be found everywhere from man-made buildings and works of art, to nature.

Brick wall

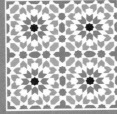

Mosaic tiles

Honeycomb

Have you seen tessellations anywhere else?

Try continuing this tessellation.

TIP: Some shapes need to be turned around to fit together.

GETTING IRREGULAR

Many tessellations use REGULAR shapes, but tessellations can use IRREGULAR shapes too. Here's how to create a tessellating irregular shape.

Whatever you do to one side of the shape, you do the opposite to the other, like this...

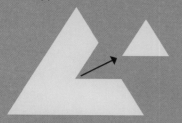

Remove a part of one side....

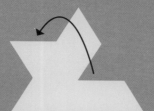

...and add it to the other side.

Then, the shapes will fit together.

Create your own irregular tessellating shape here.

Then add more copies to form a tessellation.

TESSELLATING ANIMALS

A Dutch artist named M.C. Escher is famous for his work with tessellations – especially his tessellating animals.

Escher

Go to Usborne Quicklinks to see some of my work.

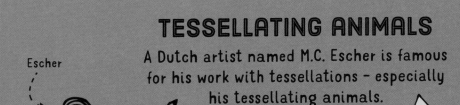

You can create tessellating animals just like the irregular shapes on the previous page. Whatever you take off one side, you add to the other.

Fish

Use this grid to create your own tessellating animals. You can use the ideas here, or make up your own.

Snake

Rhino

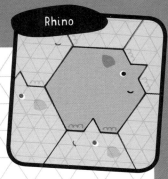

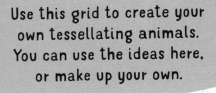

COUNT LIKE A ROMAN

The Ancient Romans used symbols for counting which we call ROMAN NUMERALS.
Use the key below to do some ancient arithmetic.

I	II	III	IV	V	VI	VII	VIII	IX	X	L	C	D	M
1	2	3	4	5	6	7	8	9	10	50	100	500	1,000

An I BEFORE a symbol means ONE LESS. IV is 1 less than V and IX is 1 less than X.

Individual symbols can be PUT TOGETHER to make bigger numbers. e.g. 7 is 5+1+1 (VII).

Big number had their own symbols.

What are these Roman numerals worth?

XXVII _____

LXI _____

DCLV _____

Work out the answers and write them in NUMBERS.

VI + VIII = _____

L - XXV = _____

What are these numbers in Roman numerals?

17 _____

23 _____

86 _____

Work out the answers and write them in ROMAN NUMERALS.

11 + 47 = _____

L x III = _____

88 ÷ 4 = _____

C - LXVI = _____

How would you write the year you were born in Roman numerals?

I, II, III, IV...

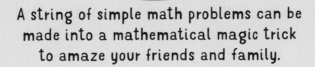

MATHEMAGICIAN

A string of simple math problems can be made into a mathematical magic trick to amaze your friends and family.

TRY THIS: Pick a number between 1 and 20 and write it in the first box below. Then, follow each step to fill in the remaining boxes.

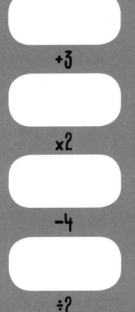

+3

x2

-4

÷2

SUBTRACT YOUR STARTING NUMBER AND THE ANSWER WILL BE...

TA DAAAA!

1

HOW DOES IT WORK?

Imagine the number you chose at the beginning is the number of marbles you have inside a bag.

+3

x2

-4

÷2

SUBTRACT WHAT YOU STARTED WITH.

The number you start with always disappears by the end, leaving just 1.

MAKE YOUR OWN TRICK

You can make up your OWN trick in the same way, picturing the starting number as the number of marbles inside a bag. Just make sure the bag disappears by the end.

INSTRUCTIONS

PICTURE OF RESULTS

1. THINK OF A NUMBER BETWEEN 1-20.

2.

3.

4.

5.

ANSWER IS ALWAYS...

Try out your trick on friends or family and watch their jaws drop.

MATHEMAGICAL CARDS

There are 5 number cards on the next page. Copy the template, or print it from the Usborne QUICKLINKS website, and cut out the cards.

Ask a friend to think of a number between 1 and 30.

Show the cards and ask your friend to pick out the ones with that number on them.

Take those cards and add up the numbers in the top left-hand corners.

14

8 + 4 + 2 =

14

THE RESULT will be your friend's number.

HOW DOES IT WORK?

Every number between 1 and 30 can be made by adding together some combination of ① ② ④ ⑧ ⑯ (the numbers in the top left-hand corners of the cards). There's only ONE way to make each number using these values, so there's only one combination of cards for the number your friend picks. Here are all the combinations. Fill in the gaps.

1 = 1	11 = 8 + 2 + 1	21 = ○ + ○ + ○
2 = 2	12 = ○ + ○	22 = 16 + 4 + 2
3 = 2 + 1	13 = ○ + ○ + ○	23 = 16 + 4 + 2 + 1
4 = 4	14 = 8 + 4 + 2	24 = ○ + ○
5 = 4 + 1	15 = ○ + ○ + ○ + ○	25 = 16 + 8 + 1
6 = ○ + ○	16 = 16	26 = 16 + 8 + 2
7 = ○ + ○ + ○	17 = 16 + 1	27 = 16 + 8 + 2 + 1
8 = 8	18 = ○ + ○	28 = ○ + ○
9 = 8 + 1	19 = 16 + 2 + 1	29 = 16 + 8 + 4 + 1
10 = 8 + 2	20 = 16 + 4	30 = ○ + ○ + ○ + ○

MATHEMAGICAL CARD SET

8	9	10
11	12	13
14	15	24
25	26	27
28	29	30

16	17	18
19	20	21
22	23	24
25	26	27
28	29	30

6	13	20	23	30
5	12	15	22	29
4	7	14	21	28

6	11	18	23	30
3	10	15	22	27
2	7	14	19	26

5	11	17	23	29
3	9	15	21	27
1	7	13	19	25

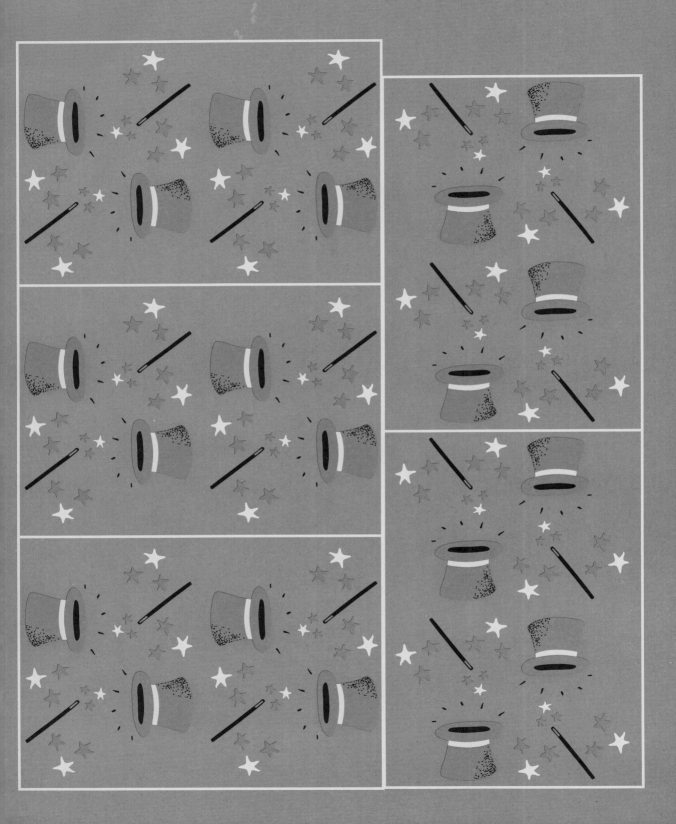

DOUBLE TROUBLE

The CHESSBOARD PROBLEM is a famous math problem. Imagine a chessboard with one grain of rice on the first square, two on the next, four on the next, and so on. How much rice would you have in total by the end of the board?

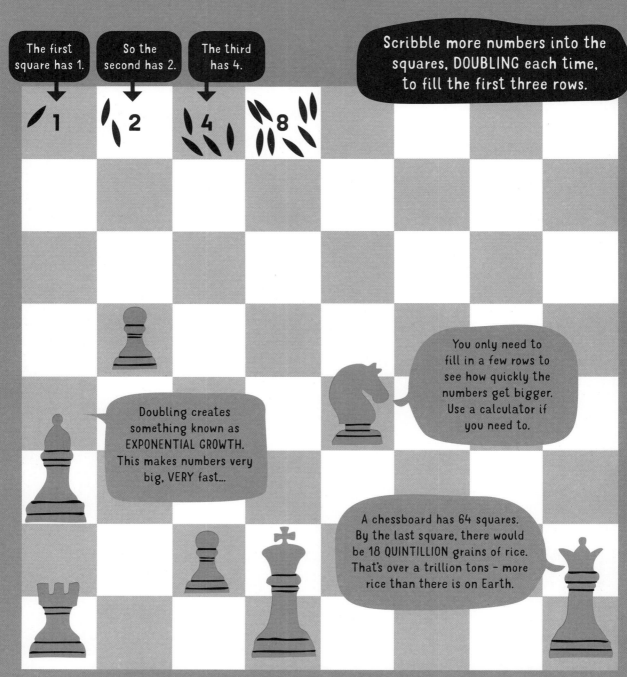

The first square has 1.

So the second has 2.

The third has 4.

1 2 4 8

Scribble more numbers into the squares, DOUBLING each time, to fill the first three rows.

You only need to fill in a few rows to see how quickly the numbers get bigger. Use a calculator if you need to.

Doubling creates something known as EXPONENTIAL GROWTH. This makes numbers very big, VERY fast...

A chessboard has 64 squares. By the last square, there would be 18 QUINTILLION grains of rice. That's over a trillion tons – more rice than there is on Earth.

ANYBODY OUT THERE?

Mathematicians can ESTIMATE things that can't be measured, using information they DO have. For example, Frank Drake designed a way to estimate the number of planets in a galaxy with life forms that could communicate with us. Try out this simplified version, for an imaginary galaxy on these pages.

1: NUMBER OF PLANETS

Experts start by working out HOW MANY planets there are in a galaxy. Count the planets on these pages. Write the answer here.

2: POTENTIAL FOR LIFE

This is the fraction of planets that in theory could SUPPORT LIFE. To create the fraction:

Count the number of planets in the GREEN BAND and put the number here.

Put the total number of planets here.

To make things easier later, you need this fraction as a decimal. Work it out by dividing the TOP by the BOTTOM, with a calculator.

3: ACTUAL LIFE

This is the fraction of those planets experts think DO actually DEVELOP life. Create it like this:

Count the number of planets with a sign of life.

Put the number of planets in the green band here.

Now turn it into a decimal:

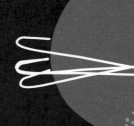

4: INTELLIGENCE

This is the fraction of planets that could develop INTELLIGENT life. Experts have to try to estimate this.

We've imagined an estimated figure for this particular galaxy.

0.8

5: TECHNOLOGY

This is the fraction of planets experts think could support life INTELLIGENT enough to create technology to COMMUNICATE with humans.

Here's an imagined figure for this one too.

0.625

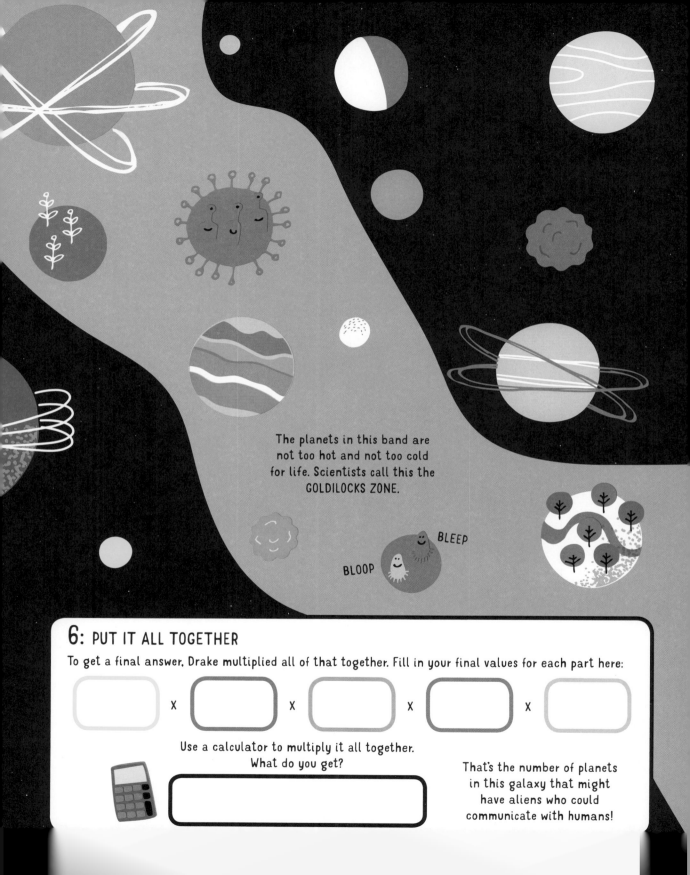

The planets in this band are not too hot and not too cold for life. Scientists call this the GOLDILOCKS ZONE.

BLEEP

BLOOP

6: PUT IT ALL TOGETHER

To get a final answer, Drake multiplied all of that together. Fill in your final values for each part here:

[ ] X [ ] X [ ] X [ ] X [ ]

Use a calculator to multiply it all together.
What do you get?

[ ]

That's the number of planets in this galaxy that might have aliens who could communicate with humans!

SYMMETRICAL SHAPES

If a shape is SYMMETRICAL, it means it looks the SAME
when it is REFLECTED or ROTATED.

REFLECTIONAL SYMMETRY

Shapes with reflectional symmetry look the same on either side of an imaginary line – as if REFLECTED in a mirror.

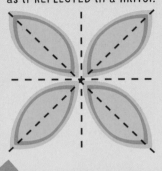

Each dotted line marks one line of symmetry.

ROTATIONAL SYMMETRY

Shapes with rotational symmetry look the same when ROTATED or turned around.

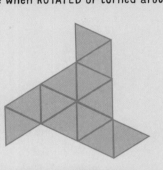

Imagine a black dot in one corner. Follow the dot as the shape turns. It moves, but the OUTLINE of the shape stays the same.

Finish off the designs below so they have REFLECTIONAL symmetry.

Most animals, including humans, have REFLECTIONAL symmetry – their bodies are the same on the left and right.

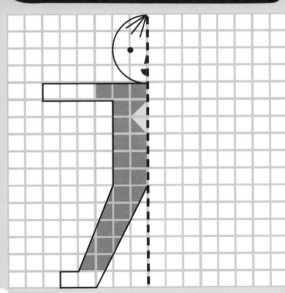

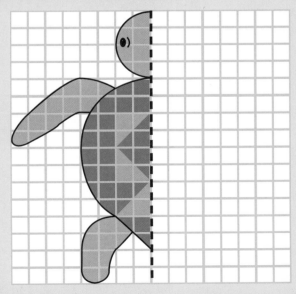

Reflectional AND rotational symmetry can be used to create round patterns known as MANDALAS. Try to match all the squares and finish this one off.

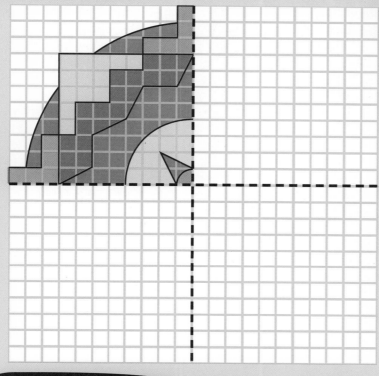

Look at the shapes below. Which description matches each shape?

Design your own symmetrical shape here.

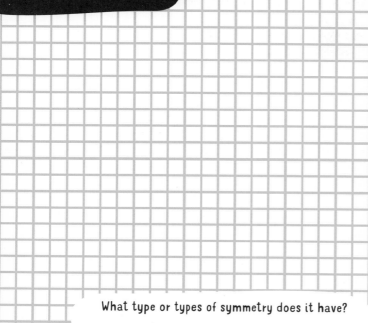

What type or types of symmetry does it have?

1.
Reflectional symmetry but NOT rotational symmetry

2.
Reflectional AND rotational symmetry

3.
Rotational symmetry but NOT reflectional symmetry

4.
No symmetry at all

GOING ON FOREVER

One of the weirdest ideas in mathematics is the concept of INFINITY - the idea that you can keep counting up and up forever.

INFINITELY BIG

Write the biggest number you can here:

Now imagine adding 1 to that number to make it even BIGGER. And you can keep adding 1, again... and again... FOREVER.

This is what mathematicians mean when they talk about INFINITY. It's the IDEA that numbers go on and on forever - there is no 'biggest' number.

Draw it yourself here.

This is the symbol used for infinity.

You can keep drawing over and over it without your pencil ever leaving the paper. The symbol goes on forever, just like the idea.

INFINITELY SMALL

Imagine a frog jumping to catch a fly, and that each leap the frog takes is exactly HALF the distance of the leap before it.

Scribble in more jumps. If the frog kept jumping, would it ever catch the fly?

YES / NO

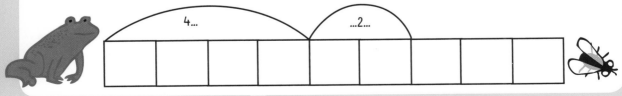

4...   ...2...

The frog's jumps keep halving and halving, becoming INFINITELY SMALL. The jumps will go on FOREVER, getting smaller and smaller.

This is a version of an ancient thought experiment known as ZENO'S PARADOX.

MÖBIUS STRIPS

An ordinary strip of paper has TWO SIDES. By adding a simple twist, you turn it into a curious, ONE-SIDED object, known as a MÖBIUS STRIP.

WHAT A TWIST

Side 1   Side 2

You will need a strip of paper about this size. Make your own or download the template from Usborne QUICKLINKS, and cut it out.

If you've made your own, mark A and B in opposite corners.

Bend the strip into a loop, with a HALF TWIST, so points A and B are TOUCHING. Stick the ends together.

You have now made a
MÖBIUS STRIP.

Try drawing a line along the MIDDLE of your strip.

Can you draw all the way around the strip without taking your pencil off the paper?

YES / NO

The strip was first developed in 1858 by two German mathematicians named Möbius and Listing.

HOW DOES IT WORK?

Adding a half twist turns your TWO-SIDED strip of paper into a ONE-SIDED loop, so you CAN draw around it.

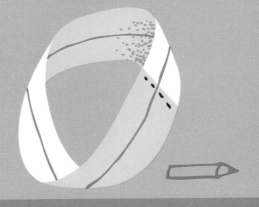

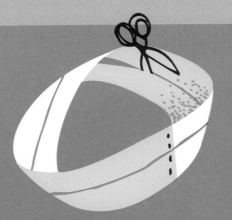

SPLITTING THE STRIP

Try cutting your Möbius strip in half along the line you just drew.

You might expect to end up with two smaller loops but in fact...

...you end up with one BIG loop.

Now try drawing a line along the middle of the new big loop. Can you still draw all the way around without taking your pencil off the paper?

YES / NO

WHAT'S CHANGED?

Cutting the strip turned your one-sided loop back into a two-sided loop, so you CAN'T draw all the way around it.

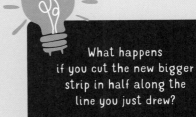

What happens if you cut the new bigger strip in half along the line you just drew?

BREAKTHROUGH

Can you match the mathematicians to the mathematical discovery, breakthrough or invention they made?

I'm an Iranian mathematician who did ground-breaking research in geometry (shapes and surfaces). I was the first woman to win the Field Medal for math in 2014.

I'm an Ancient Greek mathematician who worked out how to calculate the area of a circle, and the surface area and volume of a sphere.

MARYAM MIRZAKHANI

ARCHIMEDES

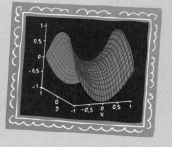
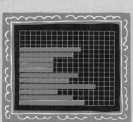

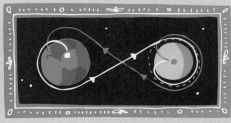

I'm an Indian mathematician who was the first to use ZERO as a number, and do arithmetic with it, 1,400 years ago. I called it "shunya," which means empty.

KATHERINE JOHNSON

WILLIAM PLAYFAIR

I'm an American mathematician who planned NASA's first manned space flight and calculated rocket paths to the Moon.

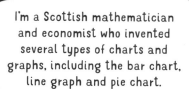

I'm a Scottish mathematician and economist who invented several types of charts and graphs, including the bar chart, line graph and pie chart.

BRAHMAGUPTA

MATH LADDERS

Starting at the top, follow each math ladder downwards to work out the final answer. Use the space around the edges to scribble your working out.

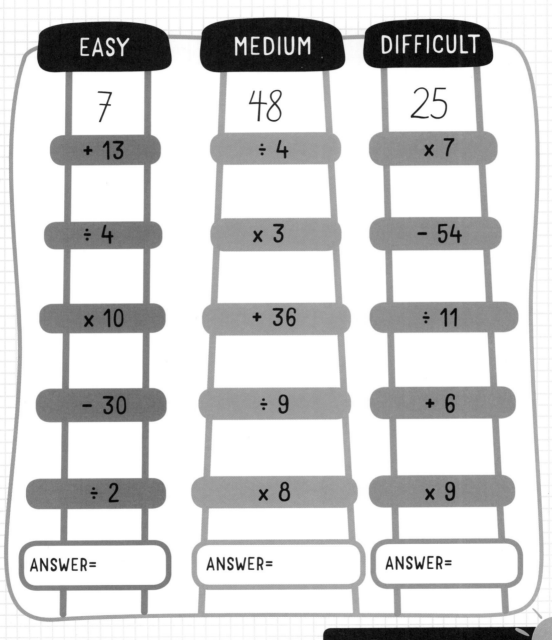

EASY

7

+ 13

÷ 4

× 10

− 30

÷ 2

ANSWER=

MEDIUM

48

÷ 4

× 3

+ 36

÷ 9

× 8

ANSWER=

DIFFICULT

25

× 7

− 54

÷ 11

+ 6

× 9

ANSWER=

Try making up your own math ladder for someone else to try.

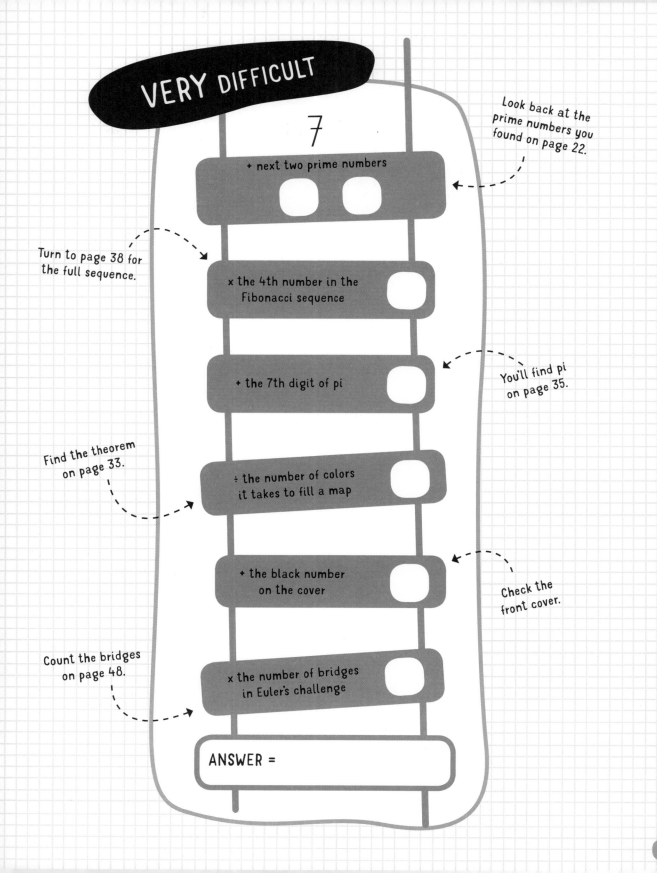

VERY DIFFICULT

7

+ next two prime numbers

Look back at the prime numbers you found on page 22.

Turn to page 38 for the full sequence.

x the 4th number in the Fibonacci sequence

+ the 7th digit of pi

You'll find pi on page 35.

Find the theorem on page 33.

÷ the number of colors it takes to fill a map

+ the black number on the cover

Check the front cover.

Count the bridges on page 48.

x the number of bridges in Euler's challenge

ANSWER =

BRAIN TEASERS

Mathematicians have to be LOGICAL, METHODICAL, and CREATIVE when solving problems. Think like a mathematician to crack the puzzles below.

REARRANGE

Can you MOVE TWO of these lines to different positions, to create SEVEN squares?

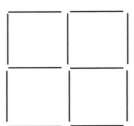

TRIANGLE TRICKS

How can you arrange these two triangles to make a star?

PYRAMID PUZZLE

In this pyramid, each block is the SUM of the two squares below it. What number goes in the blue box?

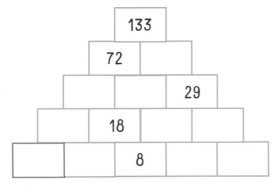

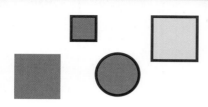

ODD ONE OUT?

ALL of these shapes can be the odd one out.
What makes each of them odd?

SO MANY SQUARES

How many squares are there here?

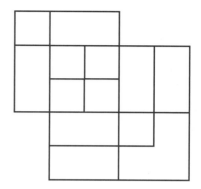

CATCH THEM ALL

With just FOUR STRAIGHT lines,
find a route through ALL the dots,
without taking the pencil off the page.

TIP: think outside the box...

SUDOKU

Finish this grid so that each column, row and
square contains the numbers 1 to 4 just once.

3			2
	4	1	
	3	2	
4			1

Try and make up your
own brain teasers to
test someone else.

6–8 PENTOMINO PROBLEMS

Here's how to finish off the started puzzle.

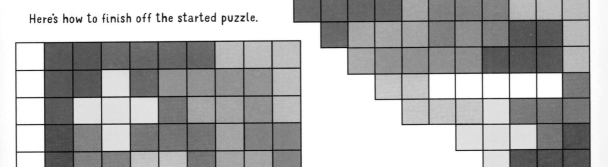

To see the MANY ways you can complete the full puzzle, go to Usborne QUICKLINKS.

This is the solution to the triangular pentomino puzzle.

9 NUMBER BUILDER

There are several ways to solve each one. There are two methods shown here, but you may have found another that works.

EASY

METHOD 1

$5 \times 20 = 100$

$100 + 1 = 101$

METHOD 2

$45 + 5 = 50$

$50 \times 2 = 100$

$100 + 1 = 101$

MEDIUM

METHOD 1

$4 \times 6 = 24$

$2 \times 5 = 10$

$24 \times 10 = 240$

$240 + 9 = 249$

METHOD 2

$5 \times 4 = 20$

$20 \times 12 = 240$

$240 + 9 = 249$

DIFFICULT

METHOD 1

$7 + 6 = 13$

$13 \times 7 = 91$

$91 + 4 = 95$

METHOD 2

$7 \times 6 = 42$

$7 \times 7 = 49$

$42 + 49 = 91$

$91 + 4 = 95$

10-11 SMALL WORLD

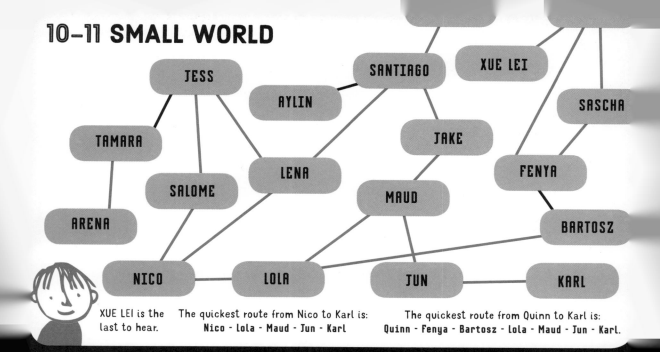

XUE LEI is the last to hear.

The quickest route from Nico to Karl is:
Nico - Lola - Maud - Jun - Karl

The quickest route from Quinn to Karl is:
Quinn - Fenya - Bartosz - Lola - Maud - Jun - Karl.

14-15 CRACKING CODES

TRANSPOSITION CIPHERS

2	4	6	8	10
6	10	14	18	22

5	6	7	8	9
25	36	49	64	81

SUBSTITUTION CIPHERS

1	2	3	4	5
A	B	C	D	E

9	8	7	6	5
L	K	J	I	H

CIPHER 1:
-2

CIPHER 2:
x2, then +2

CIPHER 3:
corresponding letter of the alphabet, where the alphabet is in reverse

16-17 INSIDE SHAPES

The area of the shed is 21ft², so it is suited to ROSIE.

18 MAGIC SQUARES

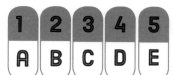

4	9	2
3	5	7
8	1	6

7	12	1	14
2	13	8	11
16	3	10	5
9	6	15	4

2	7	12	13
16	9	6	3
5	4	15	10
11	14	1	8

19 ANGLE NAVIGATOR

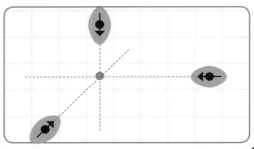

22 PRIME NUMBERS

These are the 25 prime numbers between 1 and 100.

1	2	3	4	5	6	7	8	9	10
11	12	13	14	15	16	17	18	19	20
21	22	23	24	25	26	27	28	29	30
31	32	33	34	35	36	37	38	39	40
41	42	43	44	45	46	47	48	49	50
51	52	53	54	55	56	57	58	59	60
61	62	63	64	65	66	67	68	69	70
71	72	73	74	75	76	77	78	79	80
81	82	83	84	85	86	87	88	89	90
91	92	93	94	95	96	97	98	99	100

30-32 REP-TILES

Add the two extra triangles here.

This is a HEXAGON (a shape with 6 straight sides).

It's known as an IRREGULAR hexagon as it's sides aren't all the same length.

This shape is a TRAPEZIUM (a 4-sided shape with 2 parallel sides).

23 SQUARES AND CUBES

The only two-digit square AND cube number is 64.

$$8^2 = 64 \qquad 4^3 = 64$$

The three digit square AND cube number is 729.

34-35 DISCOVER PI

GRAY CIRCLE
Diameter = 85mm (or 8.5cm)
Circumference = 267mm (26.7cm)
Circumference ÷ diameter = 3.141176 ~ 3.14

RED CIRCLE
Diameter = 64mm (or 6.4cm)
Circumference = 201mm (20.1cm)
Circumference ÷ diameter = 3.140625 ~ 3.14

BLUE CIRCLE
Diameter = 50mm (or 5cm)
Circumference = 157mm (15.7cm)
Circumference ÷ diameter = 3.14

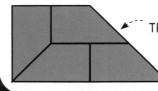

36–37 FINDING YOUR WAY

The quickest route is YELLOW.

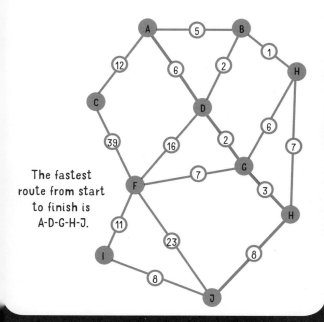

The fastest route from start to finish is A-D-G-H-J.

38–39 THE FIBONACCI SEQUENCE

The sequence goes:
0, 1, 1, 2, 3, 5, 8, 13, 21, 34, 55

The aloe has 5 spirals.

The pinecone has 13 spirals.

44–45 MICRO TO TERA

1,000 bytes = 10^3
1,000,000 bytes = 10^6
1,000,000,000 bytes = 10^9
1,000,000,000,000 bytes = 10^{12}

46–47 PATTERN HUNTING

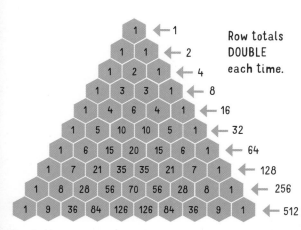

Row totals DOUBLE each time.

Here's the missing row:

1	9	36	84	126	126	84	36	9	1		
1	10	45	120	210	252	210	120	45	10	1	
1	11	55	165	330	462	462	330	165	55	11	1

48–49 TAKING A WALK

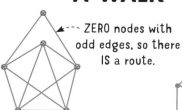

ZERO nodes with odd edges, so there IS a route.

SIX nodes with odd edges so there is NO route.

51 PERFECT NUMBERS

12
FACTORS:
1, 2, 3, 4, 6, (12)
SUM: 16
PERFECT: NO

50
FACTORS:
1, 2, 5, 10, 25, (50)
SUM: 43
PERFECT: NO

28
FACTORS:
1, 2, 4, 7, 14, (28)
SUM: 28
PERFECT: YES

36
FACTORS:
1, 2, 3, 4, 6, 9, 12, 18, (36)
SUM: 55
PERFECT: NO

55 COUNT LIKE A ROMAN

XXVII = 27

LXI = 61

DCLV = 655

17 = XVII

23 = XXIII

86 = LXXXVI

VI + VIII = 14

L - XXV = 25

11 + 47 = LVIII

L x III = CL

88 ÷ 4 = XXII

C - LXVI = XXXIV

56–60 MATHEMAGICIAN
Here are the missing sums.

6 = 4 + 2

7 = 4 + 2 + 1

12 = 8 + 4

13 = 8 + 4 + 1

15 = 8 + 4 + 2 + 1

18 = 16 + 2

21 = 16 + 4 + 1

24 = 16 + 8

28 = 16 + 8 + 4

30 = 16 + 8 + 4 + 2

61 DOUBLE TROUBLE

1	2	4	8	16	32	64	128
256	512	1,024	2,048	4,096	8,192	16,384	32,768
65,536	131,072	262,144	524,288	1,048,576	2,097,152	4,194,304	8,388,608

62–63 ANYBODY OUT THERE?
The final equation should look like this:

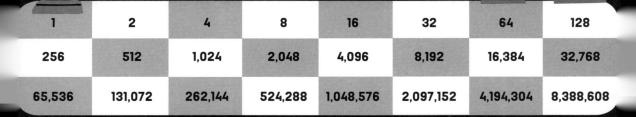

20 x 0.4 x 0.5 x 0.8 x 0.625 = 2 PLANETS

64–65 SYMMETRICAL SHAPES

1 2 3 4

69 BREAKTHROUGH

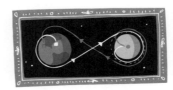

KATHERINE JOHNSON

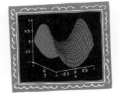

ARCHIMEDES

WILLIAM PLAYFAIR

MARYAM MIRZAKHANI

BRAHMAGUPTA

70–71 MATH LADDERS

EASY
7
+ 13
20
÷ 4
5
× 10
50
- 30
20
÷ 2
ANSWER =
10

MEDIUM
48
÷ 4
12
× 3
36
+ 36
72
÷ 9
8
× 8
ANSWER =
64

DIFFICULT
25
× 7
175
- 54
121
÷ 11
11
+ 6
17
× 9
ANSWER =
153

VERY DIFFICULT
7
+ next two prime numbers 11 13
31
× the 4th number in the Fibonacci sequence 2
62
+ the 7th digit of pi 2
64
÷ the number of colors it takes to fill a map 4
16
+ the black number on the cover 5
21
× the number of bridges in Euler's challenge 7
ANSWER = 147

REARRANGE

Here's how to move two sticks to create seven squares.

TRIANGLE TRICKS

The star is made like this.

PYRAMID PUZZLE

The finished pyramid looks like this.

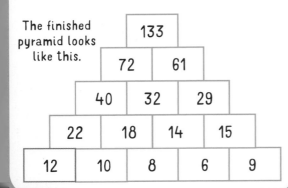

133

72 — 61

40 — 32 — 29

22 — 18 — 14 — 15

12 — 10 — 8 — 6 — 9

ODD ONE OUT?

This is odd as it's smallest.

This is odd as it has no outline.

This is odd as it's a circle.

This is odd as it's yellow.

SO MANY SQUARES

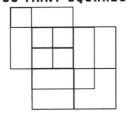

There are 17 squares here.

CATCH THEM ALL

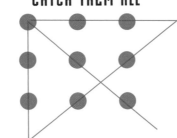

SUDOKU

3	1	4	2
2	4	1	3
1	3	2	4
4	2	3	1

Photographic credits: p.39 – Spiral aloe plant © tilt&shift / Stockimo / Alamy Stock Photo
Pinecone © Bringolo/Alamy Stock Photo.

First published in 2019 by Usborne Publishing Ltd., Usborne House, 83-85 Saffron Hill, London EC1N 8RT, England. www.usborne.com. Copyright © 2019 Usborne Publishing Ltd.